CHASING VERMEER

by
Blue Balliett

Student Packet

Written by
Linda Herman

Contains masters for:

	2 Prereading Activities
	8 Vocabulary Activities
	1 Study Guide
	2 Literary Analysis Activities
	1 Character Analysis Activity
	1 Comprehension Activity
	1 Writing Activity
	2 Quizzes
	1 Novel Test
	1 Alternative Essay Assessment
PLUS	Detailed Answer Key
	and Scoring Rubric

Note

The Scholastic, Apple Paperbacks edition of the book, published by Scholastic Inc., © 2004, was used to prepare this guide.
Novel ISBN 0-439-37297-6

Please note: Please assess the appropriateness of this book for the age level and maturity of your students prior to reading and discussing it with them.

ISBN-10: 1-58130-925-2
ISBN-13: 978-1-58130-925-6

To order, contact your local school supply store, or—

Novel Units, Inc.
P.O. Box 97
Bulverde, TX 78163-0097

Web site: www.novelunits.com

Lori Mammen, Editorial Director
Andrea M. Harris, Production Manager/Production Specialist
Taylor Henderson, Product Development Specialist
Heather M. Marnan, Product Development Specialist
Suzanne K. Mammen, Curriculum Specialist
Pamela Rayfield, Product Development Specialist
Jill Reed, Product Development Specialist
Adrienne Speer, Production Specialist

What Would You Do?

Directions: Write a brief answer telling what you would do in each of the following situations.

1. You receive a mysterious letter.

2. You see live animals falling from the sky.

3. You discover a friend's phone is disconnected.

4. You read someone else's mail without permission.

5. You sneak into a museum after hours.

6. You are chased by a criminal.

7. You find a missing friend's sweatshirt.

8. You spy on friends and family.

Name _____

Directions: Choose five chapter titles from the novel's table of contents and list them on the lines below. Write what you predict will happen in each chapter.

1. _____

_____

_____

_____

2. _____

_____

_____

_____

3. _____

_____

_____

_____

4. _____

_____

_____

_____

5. _____

_____

_____

_____

Vocabulary Word Map

discriminating (1)	convention (1)	pretentious (2)	agitated (3)
coincidence (3)	gullible (4)	relevant (6)	papyrus (7)
petroglyphs (7)	brutal (9)	exceptionally (11)	collaborations (11)
mediocre (11)	labyrinth (14)	pathetic (20)	sophisticated (21)
stupendous (23)	hybrid (23)	restricted (32)	tittered (32)

Directions: Choose 15 words from the vocabulary list with which you are unfamiliar. Complete a word map for each word. Begin by copying the sentence from the novel that contains the vocabulary word. Write what you think the word means from the way it is used in the story. Then write the word's definition as it is given in the dictionary. Compare your definition with the one from the dictionary.

Sentence from novel

_____

_____

_____

Vocabulary Word

Definition in your own words

_____

_____

_____

Definition from the dictionary

_____

_____

_____

Name _____

amber (40)	distorted (41)	frenzied (42)	capering (42)
exasperations (42)	economics (42)	underlying (42)	luminous (43)
disoriented (43)	profound (44)	senility (44)	incompetence (44)
credulity (44)	premises (44)	innumerable (45)	exhilarating (49)
inlaid (51)	compass (51)	rhombi (54)	polygons (54)

Directions: Select pairs of vocabulary words that have something in common. Then complete each sentence by explaining why the words go together.

Example: *Frenzied* and *disoriented* go together because someone might be *frenzied* because they are *disoriented*.

1. _____ and _____ go together because

_____.

2. _____ and _____ go together because

_____.

3. _____ and _____ go together because

_____.

4. _____ and _____ go together because

_____.

5. _____ and _____ go together because

_____.

6. _____ and _____ go together because

_____.

7. _____ and _____ go together because

_____.

On another sheet of paper, write sentences using the vocabulary words you did not use above.

anonymous (61)	retrieved (62)	inexplicable (62)	scoured (64)
cumulus (70)	symmetry (74)	instinctively (79)	lurch (80)
caption (80)	lute (81)	distracted (83)	superstitious (84)
baptized (86)	director (86)	guild (87)	overlap (89)

A. Directions: Look up the vocabulary words in a dictionary, and then answer the questions below. On a separate sheet of paper, explain your answer choices.

1. Would a criminal wish to remain <u>anonymous</u>?

2. Can you name three items that might be <u>retrieved</u> by a dog?

3. Is a solved mystery <u>inexplicable</u>?

4. Does <u>scoured</u> describe a mood or action?

5. Are <u>cumulus</u> clouds puffy or wispy?

6. Is the American flag or the Canadian flag a better example of <u>symmetry</u>?

B. Directions: On each line, circle the word that is not related to the vocabulary word as it is used in the novel.

7. **instinctively**	naturally	hardly	reflexively
8. **lurch**	jump	judge	jab
9. **caption**	prisoner	heading	legend
10. **lute**	instrument	wealth	music
11. **distracted**	heartfelt	preoccupied	removed
12. **superstitious**	fearful	belief	scientific
13. **baptized**	named	barred	christened
14. **director**	artist	leader	administrator
15. **guild**	blame	trade	organization
16. **overlap**	coincide	extend	defeat

Name _____

restless (90)	absentmindedly (90)	warping (90)	teleportation (90)
muffled (93)	solitaire (97)	curators (100)	indescribable (100)
conservators (101)	ingenious (105)	audible (105)	attribute (108)
obscurity (109)	instantaneous (111)	attribution (114)	insights (115)
crescent (115)	judiciously (119)	pewter (121)	subdued (123)

Directions: Write each vocabulary word in the left-hand column of the chart. Complete the chart by placing a check mark in the column that best describes your familiarity with each word. Working with a partner, find and read the line where each word appears in the story. Find the meaning of each word in the dictionary. Together with your partner, choose ten of the words checked in the last column. On a separate sheet of paper, use each of those words in a sentence.

Vocabulary Word	I Can Define	I Have Seen/Heard	New Word For Me

Vocabulary Concentration

undercurrent (127)	honorable (127)	queasy (128)	demonstrations (130)
publicity (132)	indelible (134)	massive (134)	plurality (134)
hefty (135)	pulse (143)	accusations (144)	glowered (144)
traitor (145)	midst (145)	slithered (145)	crimson (146)
dismal (148)	gargoyles (151)	turret (151)	emphasis (153)

Directions: Working with a partner, make two sets of cards. On one set, write each vocabulary word (one word per card). On the second set, write each vocabulary word's definition (one definition per card; Only write on one side of the card).

Object of Game: Match vocabulary words with their definitions by remembering each card's location.

Game Instructions: Shuffle both sets of cards together. Spread the cards face down on a table. The first player turns over two cards. If the cards match a vocabulary word with its definition, the player keeps both cards and takes another turn. If the cards don't match, return them to their places face down on the table. The second player takes a turn. Continue playing until all cards have been matched correctly. The player with the most cards wins.

Name _____

radical (154)	quadrangle (154)	mantel (154)	colleague (154)
geologists (157)	reminiscing (157)	conspicuous (163)	emerged (165)
caviar (169)	vigorously (169)	murky (172)	forgers (172)
irresistible (172)	imperious (175)	consequences (177)	jostled (179)
correspondence (182)	brusque (182)	intensely (182)	frigid (183)

A. Directions: Unscramble the vocabulary words using the definitions as clues.

1. _____ lelucoage — person somebody works with

2. _____ stegoolgis — people who study the physical history of Earth

3. _____ unsoupocics — easily seen; visible

4. _____ crilada — change from traditional forms

5. _____ ingrimesinc — remembering the past

6. _____ tamlen — frame around a fireplace

7. _____ megreed — appeared from behind something

8. _____ granuqlade — figure with four sides and four angles

B. Directions: An analogy is the same relationship between two sets of words. Use the vocabulary words above to complete the following analogies.
Examples: UP is to DOWN as IN is to OUT. (The word pairs are antonyms.)
LAVENDER is to PURPLE as PINK is to RED. (The word pairs are similar.)

9. _____ is to SUBMISSIVE as STRONG is to WEAK.

10. SHARP is to GENTLE as _____ is to PATIENT.

11. CAUSE is to EFFECT as ACTIONS are to _____.

12. EGG is to CHICKEN as _____ is to SALMON.

13. GLACIER is to _____ as VOLCANO is to FIERY.

14. CREATION is to ARTISTS as IMITATION is to _____.

15. E-MAIL is to _____ as JET is to TRANSPORTATION.

On another sheet of paper, write three original analogies using vocabulary words that you did not use above.

Name _____

compartments (188)	casement (189)	indications (191)	Gothic (191)
idyllic (192)	propelled (192)	frayed (192)	intricately (195)
obliviously (196)	collaborating (198)	overwrought (198)	rational (200)
infectious (201)	valid (204)	resolved (204)	ruthless (205)
sulky (205)	outcroppings (209)	rambling (210)	stashing (212)

A. Directions: Use the context of the sentences to fill in the missing vocabulary words.

1. _____ curtains framed the _____ windows.

2. If the women had been _____, the terrible incident would not have happened.

3. Menacing clouds and cold wind were the only _____ of the approaching storm.

4. The time warp _____ the spacecraft into the future.

5. Rain seeped into the storage _____, soaking the furniture inside.

6. The countries _____ the border dispute after two decades of war.

7. His _____ laughter broke the tension filling the room.

8. The monument's _____-lettered sign told of the soldier's sacrifice.

9. The lottery winner replaced her rigid work schedule with an _____ vacation.

10. A prescription isn't _____ without a doctor's signature.

11. No one suspected the _____ planned prank with its elaborate details.

12. _____ with emotion, she stared at the plaque that was dedicated to her.

13. It isn't _____ to _____ step off the curb into the street.

B. Directions: On another sheet of paper, use the following words in a short story or poem: ruthless, sulky, outcroppings, rambling, and stashing. Show that you know the meanings of the words as they are used in the novel.

Name _____

preoccupied (214)	corridor (218)	arbor (218)	cavernous (218)
methodically (219)	splintery (221)	clarity (221)	flurry (229)
assault (230)	indulgently (230)	unconscious (236)	idealistic (238)
reclusive (239)	speculated (240)	recipients (243)	eerie (243)
intrigued (244)	wistful (244)	pigment (247)	pun (247)

Directions: Summarize the ending of *Chasing Vermeer*. Use at least 15 vocabulary words in your summary.

_____

_____

_____

_____

_____

_____

_____

_____

_____

_____

_____

_____

_____

_____

_____

_____

© Novel Units, Inc.

Directions: Answer the following questions on a separate sheet of paper. Starred questions indicate thought or opinion questions. Use your answers in class discussions, for writing assignments, and to review for tests.

Chapters One–Three, pp. 1–34

1. Where are the letters delivered?

2. How many people receive a letter?

3. What is the letter about?

4. What does the man think about that the women do not?

5. Why isn't Ms. Hussey a disappointment?

6. Whose teaching ideas does Ms. Hussey share? Who is this person?

7. What does Petra love and Calder hate?

8. What assignment does Ms. Hussey give her class?

9. What did Calder's grandmother once tell him?

10. How do Petra and Calder feel about each other?

11. Who is Tommy Segovia?

12. *Why are pentominoes a perfect gift for Calder?

13. What kind of books does Ms. Hussey buy?

14. How does Petra describe her household?

15. How does Petra feel about having the same name as an ancient city?

16. Why is Calder's yard a good place to hide things?

17. Why is Petra familiar with the Art Institute?

18. Why does the museum guard escort Calder and Petra to Ms. Hussey?

Chapters Four–Six, pp. 35–60

1. Why isn't Ms. Hussey upset that the trip to the museum didn't work?

2. What conclusion does Petra reach about communication?

3. What did Picasso say about art?

4. Why does the class laugh at Calder?

5. What kind of person does Petra say she will never be?

6. What does Petra find on her way to the grocery store? Where does she find this item?

7. Where did Charles Fort collect reports of bizarre happenings?

8. *What object does Petra write about for her homework? Do you agree with her that this object could be considered art? Why or why not?

9. What sentence in *Lo!* does Petra especially like?

10. Who visits Petra just before she falls asleep? How does she describe this person's world?

11. What do Charles Fort and Petra both understand?

12. What helps Calder think?

13. *What object does Calder write about for his homework? Why does he love this object?

14. Who interrupts Calder as he works on his homework?

15. Who sends Calder a letter?

16. Who is Frog?

17. What does Calder remember about the last Fourth of July?

Chapters Seven–Nine, pp. 61–89

1. Why does Calder decide to have lunch with Petra?

2. What does Petra say Charles Fort doesn't take too seriously?

3. When does Calder tell Petra about Frog disappearing?

4. Why is Petra interested in Calder's story about Ms. Hussey, Mr. Watch, and Mrs. Sharpe?

5. What does Mrs. Sharpe say is the name of the painting on Calder's box?

6. What does Petra chase down the street but can't catch?

7. How do Vermeer's paintings make Calder feel? Why does he think there could be codes hidden in the paintings?

8. *What did Vermeer leave behind? Why might Petra like Vermeer?

9. Why do people visit Harper Avenue on Halloween?

10. What is Petra's costume?

11. What is Calder's costume?

12. Who is the lady in Petra's dream?

13. Why does Calder give Petra a piece of paper and a pencil?

14. What does Calder tell Petra about pentominoes?

15. What is the first fact Calder and Petra discover about Vermeer? Why is this spooky?

16. Why does Calder wonder if someone destroyed Vermeer's notebooks or letters?

17. Where is the painting *A Lady Writing*?

18. What item becomes Calder and Petra's symbol of secrecy?

 © Novel Units, Inc.

Chapters Ten–Twelve, pp. 90–126

1. Why does Calder want to call the National Gallery of Art?
2. What do Petra and Calder find out about *A Lady Writing*?
3. Why is Petra worried about her dad?
4. What did Calder's grandmother wish about Vermeer?
5. Why does Calder sometimes wish he'd never heard of Fort or Vermeer?
6. What is the newspaper headline on November 5?
7. Where do curators find a note from the thief? What does it say?
8. What would Calder and Petra have seen if they had looked back at the bookstore?
9. What is printed in the *Chicago Tribune*?
10. When does the thief say *A Lady Writing* will be returned?
11. What is the first thing the thief asks the public to do?
12. What is Calder's job when the class studies Vermeer's paintings? What is Petra's job?
13. What does everyone agree is the most important issue with *A Lady Writing*?
14. *Why do some people forgive the thief? Do you agree or disagree with these people?
15. How does Ms. Hussey's class vote on Vermeer's 35 paintings?
16. What does the pentomino tell Calder after tea at Mrs. Sharpe's house?
17. What happens when Calder calls Tommy?
18. Who helps Petra find a clue? What is the clue?

Chapters Thirteen–Fifteen, pp. 127–153

1. What does Ms. Hussey ask her class to imagine?
2. What happens to the note Petra passes to Calder?
3. Why doesn't Petra think the thief would ask Ms. Hussey for help?
4. From where are the thief's advertisements mailed?
5. What do the sixth graders conclude about letters?
6. What excuse does Calder use to search Mrs. Sharpe's house?
7. What does Calder discover about Mrs. Sharpe's house?
8. Why does Tommy need help? How do Calder and Petra help him?
9. Why do Calder and Petra think Mrs. Sharpe is involved with the theft?
10. Who had Mrs. Sharpe's husband been researching?

11. Why Is Ms. Hussey's class out of control?

12. Whose letter does Petra think she saw in Calder's garden?

13. Why didn't Ms. Hussey or Mrs. Sharpe do anything when they received letters from the thief?

14. Where do Calder and Petra go to talk? What do they decide?

15. Why does Calder decide the U pentomino stands for University School?

16. What is a "dark horse"?

Chapters Sixteen–Eighteen, pp. 154–187

1. What size is the painting *A Lady Writing*?

2. Why do Calder and Petra pretend to make a map of the school?

3. *Why is Calder locked in the basement?

4. How does Petra free Calder from the basement?

5. What do Calder and Petra remove from the basement?

6. What does Petra find in the bushes near Mrs. Sharpe's house?

7. Why do Calder and Petra decide not to walk around alone?

8. What word does Calder say the P pentomino stands for? What does Petra say?

9. What is *The Vermeer Dilemma* about?

10. What message does the book send to the thief?

11. Why doesn't Petra think the thief is a "sicko"?

12. Where is Mrs. Sharpe going? Why?

13. To whom is Mrs. Sharpe's letter addressed? Who stops Calder and Petra from opening the letter?

14. What does Petra tell Mrs. Sharpe about that no one knows except Calder?

15. What words does Mrs. Sharpe form with Calder's pentominoes?

16. How does Tommy discover what happened to Frog?

Chapters Nineteen–Twenty-one, pp. 188–213

1. What does Petra do as she and Calder walk down the staircase?

2. What reminds Petra of the words Mrs. Sharpe made with pentominoes?

3. Why do Calder and Petra go home through backyards?

4. After she knows they weren't followed, what does Petra tell Calder?

5. What does Petra decide about her experience on the staircase?

6. What does Petra think 12 year olds are old enough to do?

7. What feeling or image won't let Petra stop thinking?

8. What does Petra do best?

9. What newspaper article are Petra's parents reading? How does Petra's father describe the thief?

10. What does the thief demand of colleagues at the National Gallery of Art?

11. What will the thief do if the demands are not met?

12. Why does Petra suggest she and Calder call the police?

13. Why doesn't Calder want to call the police?

14. What decision do Calder and Petra make?

15. What warning does Mrs. Sharpe give Petra?

16. Who is the first person Calder and Petra run into at Delia Dell?

17. Who else does Petra see at Delia Dell? Why does this make her miserable?

18. What shocks Petra when she looks out the window?

Chapters Twenty-two–Twenty-four, pp. 214–254

1. What do Calder and Petra share?

2. What does Calder realize about the puzzle?

3. Whom do Calder and Petra watch leaving the building?

4. Why does Calder rush to the staircase?

5. Where do Calder and Petra find *A Lady Writing*?

6. *Why would Calder be relieved if the police caught them?

7. Who chases Calder and Petra through the playground?

8. How does Petra feel when she sees Calder on top of the slide?

9. Where does Petra find help? Who helps her?

10. What does Petra see when she returns to the playground?

11. Why is a man ducking out of the patrol car?

12. How does the policeman react when Petra tells him the suspect has a priceless Vermeer?

13. What does Petra see in the snow under the tree house?

14. Where does Petra find Calder? What does he have?

15. How does Calder recognize the thief?

16. What names does the thief use?

17. Why did the thief send the three letters?

18. Who makes a generous gift to the National Gallery? How is the money to be used?

19. Who are the three letter recipients? Why did Petra find a fourth letter?

20. What does Mrs. Sharpe tell Calder and Petra that she asks them to keep secret?

21. What does Calder discover about the people's names on his list?

22. What happens to *A Lady Writing*?

Literary Devices

Directions: Authors use literary devices to make their writing interesting and descriptive. Read the definitions of the literary devices listed below and then find an example of each in the novel. Include the page number where you found the example.

Flashback: The story switches to an event from the past, then returns to the present. (*Look for clues such as "She remembered the last time..." followed by a scene from the past.*)	
Foreshadowing: A hint is given before the event actually occurs. (*Example: His plan would work unless his mother found out about it.*)	
Rhetorical Question: A question is asked for effect with no answer expected. (*Example: She looked at the jagged peak and asked, "Do you think I'm part mountain goat?"*)	
Metaphor: A comparison is made between two unlike objects. (*Example: He was a human tree.*)	
Simile: A comparison is made between two unlike objects using the words "like" or "as." (*Example: The color of her eyes was like the cloudless sky.*)	
Onomatopoeia: Words sound like what they mean. (*Examples: buzz, hiss*)	
Personification: Human traits are given to an object. (*Example: The cloud cried.*)	

Name _____

Character Attribute Chart

Directions: Choose five characters from the book. List their names in the left-hand boxes. Fill in the other boxes with requested information.

Character	One-Word Description	Appearance	Significance to the Story	Do you know anyone similar?

Name _____

Connections

Directions: The following characters from the book have a connection to Vermeer. Fill in the dotted rectangles with details explaining each connection.

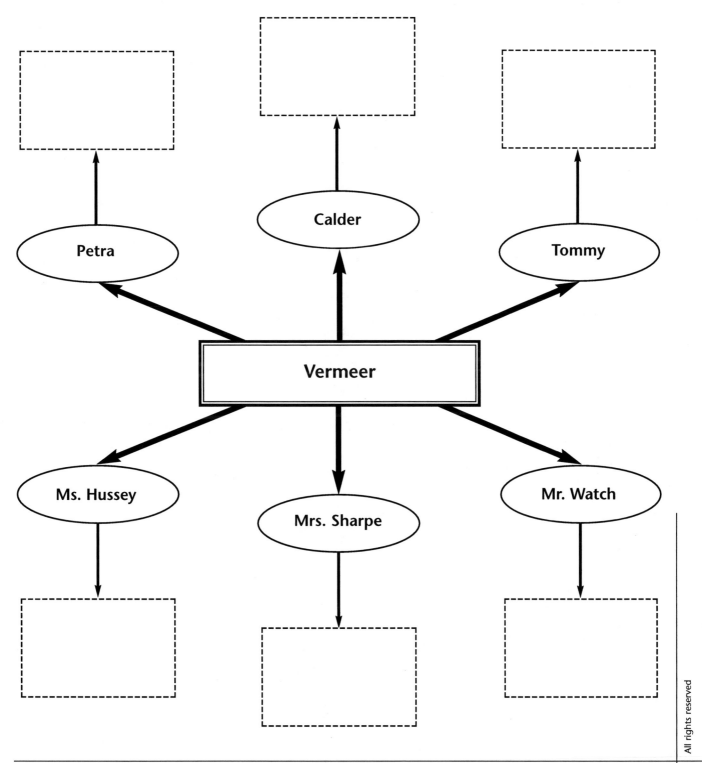

Thematic Analysis

Directions: Choose a theme from the book to be the focus of your word web. Complete the web and then answer the question in each starred box. Theme suggestions include friendship, open-mindedness, problem solving, art appreciation, and love of learning.

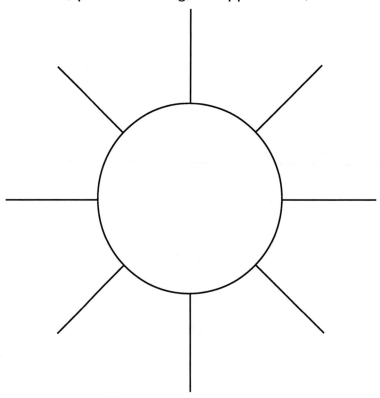

 What is the author's main message?

 What did you learn from the book?

Write a Mystery

Directions: Use the following spaces to outline a mystery story you would like to write. On a separate sheet of paper, write your mystery story.

Detectives and Suspects

_____

_____

_____

_____

Setting

_____

_____

_____

_____

Mystery to be solved

_____

_____

_____

Clues

_____

_____

_____

Red herrings

_____

_____

_____

_____

Solution

_____

_____

_____

_____

Name _____

A. Matching: Match the character names with the correct description.

____ 1. Ms. Hussey		a.	Petra's father
____ 2. Tommy		b.	bratty sixth grader
____ 3. Picasso		c.	cool teacher
____ 4. Mrs. Sharpe		d.	author of *Lo!*
____ 5. Old Fred		e.	Calder's father
____ 6. Charles Fort		f.	Tommy's stepfather
____ 7. Walter Pillay		g.	Petra's mother
____ 8. Yvette Pillay		h.	elderly woman
____ 9. Frog		i.	Calder's friend in New York
____ 10. Zelda Segovia		j.	missing boy
____ 11. Denise		k.	Calder's boss at Powell's Used Books
____ 12. Frank Andalee		l.	Calder's mother
____ 13. Norma Andalee		m.	artist who painted *The Geographer*
____ 14. Mr. Watch		n.	Tommy's mother
____ 15. Vermeer		o.	artist who said, "Art is a lie, but a lie that tells the truth."

B. Short Answer: Write your answer on the lines below.

Why does Calder carry pentominoes in his pocket?

_____

_____

_____

_____

_____

_____

Name _____

A. Sequencing: Number the following events in the order that they occurred.

____ a. Petra finds the thief's letter in a hedge near Mrs. Sharpe's house.

____ b. Calder decides the U pentomino is for University School, a brilliant hiding place.

____ c. Calder follows the thief to the tree house.

____ d. Petra sees objects matching Mrs. Sharpe's pentomino words at Delia Dell Hall.

____ e. Ms. Hussey asks the class what they would do if they received a letter from the thief.

____ f. Calder is locked in the basement of Gracie Hall.

____ g. Calder and Petra find the painting under the twelfth stair.

____ h. Petra's dad and the man with the bushy eyebrows leave Delia Dell Hall together.

____ i. The thief threatens to destroy *A Lady Writing*.

____ j. Calder and Petra learn that Mrs. Sharpe's husband was a Vermeer scholar.

B. Short Answer: Write your answer on the lines below.

Who are the three people who received letters from the thief? Explain why the thief chose each person.

_____

_____

_____

_____

_____

_____

_____

_____

_____

Name _____

A. True/False

_____ 1. Three letters are delivered one night in Philadelphia.

_____ 2. Charles Fort wrote: "We shall pick up an existence by its frogs."

_____ 3. Calder recognizes Petra's Halloween costume.

_____ 4. Blue M&Ms symbolize danger.

_____ 5. The thief claims Vermeer painted only 26 of the 35 paintings attributed to him.

_____ 6. The Lady tells Petra to search for the painting in basements.

_____ 7. Frog sends Calder a Vermeer postcard from the National Gallery of Art.

_____ 8. Petra finds 12 pearls in *A Lady Writing*.

_____ 9. Xavier Glitts plans to keep the stolen painting in his personal art collection.

_____ 10. Many wall labels on Vermeer paintings are changed to "Attributed to Johannes Vermeer."

B. Fill in the Blanks

11. Petra searches for her dad's letter in the _____.

12. The painting on Calder's box is titled _____ _____.

13. Vermeer left behind more _____ than answers.

14. Fred _____ Tommy and his mother in New York.

15. The author of *The Vermeer Dilemma* writes that the thief's mission is _____.

16. Calder realizes that the puzzle hinges on _____.

17. Petra notices a _____ inside a _____ on the staircase.

18. Calder threatens the thief that he will put his _____ through the painting.

19. Xavier Glitts' nickname is _____ Man.

20. _____ _____ _____ is returned to the National Gallery.

C. Identification: Explain how each word listed below is important to the story. Write one or two sentences for each word.

21. letters _____

_____

Name _____

22. codes _____
_____

23. pentominoes _____
_____

24. frogs _____
_____

25. blue M&Ms _____
_____

26. *Lo!* _____
_____

27. twelves _____
_____

28. coincidence _____
_____

29. attribution _____
_____

30. art _____
_____

D. Essay: Select I or II and write your response on a separate sheet of paper.

 I. Calder and Petra's relationship grows during the story. Write a two-paragraph essay that explains how Calder and Petra came to trust each other. Identify scenes in the book that support your answer.

 II. Think about events that happen in *Chasing Vermeer* and how one event causes another. Choose an event from the story. Write a one- to two-paragraph essay that explains how this event caused the others to happen. Use information from the book to support your answer.

Alternative Essay Assessment

Directions: Select I or II and write your response on a separate sheet of paper.

I. In the story, the students realize old paintings are interesting (p. 172). Write a well-developed paragraph on whether or not you think art is interesting. Explain your opinion.

II. Write a well-developed paragraph telling how art is important in people's lives. Explain how people benefit from art.

Answer Key

Activities #1–#2: Answers will vary.

Activity #3: Student definitions will vary. Dictionary definitions of the vocabulary words as used in the novel: discriminating—having excellent taste or judgment; convention—the usual way in which things are done; pretentious—an exaggeration of self-importance; agitated—excited or disturbed; coincidence—a remarkable, surprising occurrence; gullible—easily deceived; relevant—having a logical connection; papyrus—writing material made from the papyrus plant; petroglyphs—drawings made by prehistoric people; brutal—demanding, exhausting; exceptionally—unusually; collaborations—product of working together; mediocre—only ordinary; labyrinth—place with complicated paths; pathetic—inadequate, pitiful; sophisticated—refined, cultured; stupendous—grand, miraculous; hybrid—crossbreed, composite; restricted—limited, confined; tittered—snickered

Activity #4: Answers will vary.

Activity #5: A. 1. yes 2. Answers will vary. Possibilities include bone, newspaper, slippers 3. no 4. action 5. puffy 6. Canadian (same on both sides) **B.** 7. hardly 8. judge 9. prisoner 10. wealth 11. heartfelt 12. scientific 13. barred 14. artist 15. blame 16. defeat

Activity #6: Answers will vary.

Activity #7: Player with the most cards wins.

Activity #8: A. 1. colleague 2. geologists 3. conspicuous 4. radical 5. reminiscing 6. mantel 7. emerged 8. quadrangle **B.** 9. imperious 10. brusque 11. consequences 12. caviar 13. frigid 14. forgers 15. correspondence

Activity #9: A. 1. frayed, casement 2. collaborating 3. indications 4. propelled 5. compartments 6. resolved 7. infectious 8. Gothic 9. idyllic 10. valid 11. intricately 12. overwrought 13. rational, obliviously **B.** Answers will vary.

Activity #10: Answers will vary.

Study Guide
Chapters One–Three: 1. neighborhood in Chicago (p. 1) 2. three (p. 1) 3. a crime against one of the world's greatest painters (p. 1) 4. the reward (p. 3) 5. She has no idea what the class will study—it depends on what interests them, or "what gets interested in us" (p. 6). 6. John Dewey; He started University School (p. 6). 7. writing (p. 7) 8. to find a letter that changed a life, and then write her an unforgettable letter (pp. 8–9) 9. He breathed patterns the way other people breathed air (p. 9). 10. She thinks he is kind of weird, and he thinks she is exceptionally weird (pp. 10–11). 11. Calder's friend who moved away (p. 11) 12. Answers will vary, but should include that Calder loves patterns (pp. 9, 13–14). 13. murder and art (p. 16) 14. "a tornado where life swirled in noisy circles" (p. 19) 15. She likes being named after a mysterious place of buried secrets (p. 21). 16. Calder's dad tests new plants at home, making the yard a tangle of green (pp. 23–24). 17. A babysitter took her to the museum once a month (p. 28). 18. He finds Calder and Petra in a restricted storage room (p. 32).

Chapters Four–Six: 1. She enjoyed the search (p. 35). 2. It's hard to study (p. 35). 3. "Art is a lie, but a lie that tells the truth" (p. 36). 4. Calder isn't aware his hand is raised; he isn't prepared to discuss his thoughts (p. 38). 5. one who looks at art without asking questions or thinking (p. 40) 6. the book *Lo!*; in the giveaway box at Powell's bookstore (p. 41) 7. from journals and newspapers around the world (p. 43) 8. *Lo!*; Answers will vary (p. 46). 9. "We shall pick up an existence by its frogs" (p. 47). 10. a young, but old-fashioned woman; a writer's world (pp. 47–49) 11. "There is much more to be uncovered about the world than most people think" (p. 49). 12. working with pentominoes (p. 50) 13. a box with a painting on it; His grandmother gave the box to him, and he feels a sense of understanding with the man in the painting (pp. 51–52). 14. Mr. Watch, Ms. Hussey, and Mrs. Sharpe (pp. 55–56) 15. Tommy (p. 57) 16. missing kid who lives next door to Tommy (p. 56) 17. Tommy's stepfather, Old Fred, announced the family was moving to New York (p. 58).

Chapters Seven–Nine: 1. to tell her about the incident in front of his house and that he liked her writing description (p. 62) 2. anyone's thinking, including his own (p. 63) 3. after Petra reads from her book about people disappearing (p. 64) 4. Louise Coffin Sharpe is the name written in her book (p. 65) 5. *The Geographer* (p. 67) 6. a letter about an old crime and art (pp. 70–71) 7. like he is peeking in at someone's private moment; Codes involve repetition, and the same objects repeat in Vermeer's works (p. 74). 8. more questions than answers; Answers will vary, but should include that Petra likes questions better than answers (p. 75). 9. Harper Avenue families take pride in being as frightening as possible (p. 76). 10. the writing lady from her dream (pp. 77–79) 11. a red F pentomino (pp. 79–80) 12. the woman in Vermeer's painting *A Lady Writing* (p. 80) 13. to keep a record of unexplained things (p. 81) 14. Pentominoes seem to talk to him (p. 84). 15. Vermeer was baptized on Halloween. They started writing about Vermeer on the same day his name was recorded (p. 86). 16. because almost nothing is known about the artist or his life (p. 87) 17. in the National Gallery of Art in Washington, D.C. (p. 88) 18. blue M&Ms (p. 89)

Chapters Ten–Twelve: 1. to see if *A Lady Writing* is there and safe (p. 90) 2. The painting is traveling to Chicago for a show at the Art Institute (p. 92). 3. He seems to be in his own world and distracted (pp. 95–96). 4. He should have used more red in his paintings (p. 97). 5. He doesn't understand why accidental events seem to fit together (p. 98). 6. "Vermeer Vanishes: Irreplaceable Treasure Disappears Between Washington and Chicago" (p. 99) 7. taped to packing materials in the traveling case; "You will come to agree with me" (p. 101). 8. Ms. Hussey and Mr. Watch leave the store with Ms. Hussey carrying a package (pp. 107–108). 9. unsigned letter from the thief (p. 108) 10. when the lies surrounding Vermeer's work are corrected (p. 108) 11. look at Vermeer's paintings (p. 110) 12. Calder organizes data into a chart. Petra records conclusions about which paintings are "real" and which are not (pp. 112–113). 13. to get the painting back safely (p. 113) 14. The thief's mission of finding the truth is important. Answers will vary (p. 114). 15. Most students side with the thief, agreeing Vermeer's early and late works are suspicious (p. 114). 16. fooled (p. 121) 17. He gets a recording saying Tommy's phone has been disconnected (p. 123). 18. the woman in *A Lady Writing*; The painting is hidden in a place with dark wood (pp. 124–125).

Chapters Thirteen–Fifteen: 1. what they would do if they received a letter from the thief (p. 127) 2. Ms. Hussey pockets it (p. 128). 3. She's just a sixth-grade teacher (p. 129). 4. New York, Florence, and Amsterdam (p. 132) 5. Letters as a form of communication are very much alive (p. 133). 6. needs to use the bathroom (p. 137) 7. It's nothing but wooden storage places (p. 138). 8. Fred deserted Tommy and his mother. They need money to come home. They bake and sell brownies (p. 140). 9. Mrs. Sharpe received a letter from the thief and is asking for police protection (p. 140). 10. Vermeer (p. 142) 11. The class is upset that Ms. Hussey is arrested as a suspect in the theft (p. 144). 12. Ms. Hussey's (p. 145) 13. Both women were terrified (p. 146). 14. Fargo Hall; to start actively hunting for the painting (pp. 149–151) 15. The school is a brilliant place to hide the painting (pp. 152–153). 16. a difficult piece in a puzzle that isn't seen until needed (p. 153)

Chapters Sixteen–Eighteen: 1. a foot by a foot and a half (p. 154) 2. as an excuse to look around (p. 156) 3. Answers will vary, but should include Calder hides with the package when the principal returns (p. 159). 4. She steals the basement keys from the secretary's desk (p. 163). 5. an old painting of a woman done by a second grader (p. 166) 6. the thief's letter (p. 169) 7. They could end up missing like Frog (p. 170). 8. pray; prey, and "Maybe it's *pray* we're not *prey*" (p. 170). 9. positive things that have come out of the theft (p. 171) 10. The painting should be returned, and the thief should consider his mission successful (p. 173). 11. She would know if the Lady had been hurt

(p. 174). 12. the hospital; She broke her leg (p. 175). 13. Ms. Isabel Hussey; a man with an accent (pp. 176, 179) 14. her dream about the painting; Vermeer's Lady communicates with her (p. 182). 15. finds, flute, lines, filmy, tails, monkey, panel, vines, and fruit (p. 185) 16. Frog sends Tommy a postcard from the National Gallery of Art (p. 186).

Chapters Nineteen–Twenty-one: 1. stops with a jolt (p. 195) 2. a carved monkey on the staircase railing (p. 195) 3. Petra says they need to disappear (p. 196). 4. "I think we've found her" (p. 197). 5. The experience was a huge, strange coincidence (p. 198). 6. to sort out what makes sense and what doesn't (p. 199) 7. a rectangle inside a triangle (p. 200) 8. imagining (p. 200) 9. more news about the theft; a maniac; a self-absorbed lunatic (p. 201) 10. write letters stating the thief's point of view is valid and request attributions be changed (pp. 203–204) 11. destroy *A Lady Writing* (p. 204) 12. A police search would have a better chance of finding the painting (p. 205). 13. Calder is thinking about the headlines if they find the painting (p. 205). 14. If they don't find the painting today, they will talk to the police or their parents (p. 206). 15. to be careful; "Looking and seeing are two very different things" (p. 207). 16. the man from the post office (pp. 207–209) 17. Petra's dad; She can't think of a reason why her dad would be at Delia Dell (pp. 212–213). 18. Her dad is with the man from the post office. He no longer has the package (p. 213).

Chapters Twenty-two–Twenty-four: 1. birthdays (p. 214) 2. It hinges on "twelves" (p. 215). 3. the man from the post office (pp. 215–216) 4. to check the twelfth stair (p. 219) 5. in a shallow storage area behind the twelfth panel under the twelfth stair (pp. 220–221) 6. Answers will vary, but should include the police will help them. They will be in danger if the thief catches them (p. 225). 7. a man in a dark jacket (p. 226) 8. fear for Calder's safety, and admiration for his quick thinking and bravery (p. 227) 9. at the Medici Restaurant; a university police officer (p. 227) 10. Calder's bloody sweatshirt (p. 229) 11. He is stealing the painting, which Petra left in the car (pp. 229–230). 12. He doesn't believe her (p. 230). 13. man-sized boot prints (p. 233) 14. in the tree house; the painting (pp. 234–235) 15. Calder recognizes Old Fred's voice (p. 236). 16. Fred Steadman, Xavier Glitts, and Glitter Man (p. 237) 17. to confuse authorities and to create three suspects (pp. 239–240) 18. Mrs. Sharpe; to pay for Vermeer scholars to work on attribution and the crime (pp. 240–241) 19. Mrs. Sharpe, Ms. Hussey, and Mr. Watch; Mr. Watch lost the letter and a copy of the letter (pp. 242–243). 20. The woman in *A Lady Writing* "told" her to clear Vermeer's name by making sure the world knew that some of "his" paintings had been done by followers (pp. 246–247). 21. The 12 people have 12 letters in their names, and the first letters of their first names are pentominoes (pp. 248, 250). 22. The painting returns to the National Gallery (p. 254).

Activity #11: Answers will vary. Possibilities: Flashback: Calder remembers receiving his first set of pentominoes (pp.11–14). Foreshadowing: "They swore that they were going to do something important with their lives—solve a great mystery,..." (pp. 11–12); Rhetorical Question: "Would they ever study regular subjects, like the other classes did?" (p. 7); Metaphor: "...Petra was a club sandwich of cultures" (p. 20). Simile: "He looked like a lopsided bee" (p. 26). Onomatopoeia: "'What were *you* doing in there?' Petra hissed." (p. 32); Personification: "Why was yellow cheerful...?" (p. 10)

Activity #12: Answers will vary. Possibilities: Calder—logical; mutters and looks like he just woke up (p. 10); detective who uses pentominoes to solve the mystery; Petra—brainy; glasses and triangle of bouncy, curly hair (pp. 11, 77); detective who uses questions and the unexplained to solve the mystery; Ms. Hussey—progressive; long ponytail and three earrings in each ear (p. 8); letter receiver, motivates Calder and Petra to solve the mystery; Mrs. Sharpe—sharp; unusually green eyes surrounded by lots of wrinkles and bones (p. 67); letter receiver, wife of Vermeer scholar, guides Calder and Petra by giving them facts that help solve the mystery; Denise Dodge—bratty; tall (p. 20); red herring who provides conflict for Calder and Petra's growing relationship

Activity #13: Answers will vary. Possibilities: Calder—has box with *The Geographer* painted on it (p. 67); box given to him by grandmother who liked Vermeer (p. 97); his research leads to recognizing Petra's costume as *A Lady Writing* (pp. 73–75, 79–81); his idea to call museum about painting (pp. 90–93), finds and saves stolen painting (pp. 221–223, 234–235); Petra—dreams of woman in *A Lady Writing* (pp. 47–49); gets clues from the Lady (pp. 125, 193–197, 200, 232); finds and saves stolen painting (pp. 221–223, 227–229, 232–235); possibly related to Vermeer's family (p. 252); Tommy—receives postcard with Vermeer painting from Frog (pp. 186–187); stepson of thief (p. 242); Ms. Hussey—has class study Vermeer (pp. 104, 112–115); rumored that she was arrested as suspect (p. 144); receives letter from thief (p. 146); discusses Vermeer with thief, giving him the attribution idea (p. 238); Mrs. Sharpe—has a copy of *The Geographer* (p. 67); receives letter from thief (pp. 140–141); married to Vermeer scholar (pp. 141–142, 147); records messages from woman in *A Lady Writing* (pp. 246–247); Mr. Watch—wants to write a book about an art mystery (p. 239); talks to thief (p. 239); receives letter from the thief (pp. 242–243)

Activity #14: The author's main message is there are connections between seemingly unrelated events that many people miss; therefore, people should observe, question, be open-minded, and think for themselves. Answers will vary.

Activity #15: Answers will vary.

Quiz #1: A. 1. c (p. 7) 2. i (pp. 11, 14) 3. o (p. 36) 4. h (pp. 55–56) 5. f (p. 58) 6. d (p. 42) 7. e (p. 23) 8. l (p. 24) 9. j (p. 56) 10. n (p. 58) 11. b (p. 20) 12. a (p. 20) 13. g (p. 20) 14. k (p. 16) 15. m (p. 67) **B.** Answers will vary. Suggestions: Calder likes patterns and sees them everywhere. Pentominoes are patterns. Pentominoes help him think, and they tell him things (pp. 9, 13–14, 84).

Quiz #2: A. a. 5 (p. 169) b. 3 (p. 152) c. 10 (p. 234) d. 6 (pp. 195–196) e. 1 (p. 127) f. 4 (p. 160) g. 9 (pp. 219–221) h. 8 (p. 213) i. 7 (p. 204) j. 2 (pp. 141–142) **B.** Ms. Hussey—gave thief the attribution idea (p. 238); Mrs. Sharpe—widow of Vermeer scholar and passionate about Vermeer's work (p. 239); Mr. Watch—wants to write an art mystery novel (p. 239); The thief's main goal is to confuse authorities and create three suspects (p. 240).

Novel Test: A. 1. F (p. 1) 2. T (p. 42) 3. T (pp. 79–80) 4. F (p. 89) 5. T (p. 108) 6. F (p. 125) 7. F (p. 186) 8. T (p. 223) 9. F (pp. 238, 240) 10. T (p. 254) **B.** 11. garbage (p. 22) 12. *The Geographer* (p. 67) 13. questions (p. 75) 14. deserted (p. 140) 15. successful (p. 173) 16. twelves (p. 215) 17. rectangle; triangle (p. 220) 18. knee (p. 227) 19. Glitter (p. 242) 20. *A Lady Writing* (p. 254) **C.** Answers will vary. Suggestions: 21. The thief sends letters to confuse authorities and create suspects. Ms. Hussey discusses letters in her classroom. Petra searches for her dad's letter and finds a letter near Mrs. Sharpe's house (pp. 7–9, 22, 127–129, 169, 238–240). 22. Tommy's coded letters tell Calder about Frog disappearing and Fred leaving (pp. 56, 139). 23. Pentominoes help Calder think and tell him things. They provide clues that help solve the mystery (pp. 84, 95, 152, 155, 185, 214–215). 24. There are incidents of raining frogs in *Lo!*. The missing boy's name is Frog. Petra says she and Calder should have picked up on Glitter Man's existence from Frog because of Fort's sentence: "We shall pick up an existence by its frogs." Frogs are part of the hidden message in the illustrations (pp. 42, 45, 56, 252–254). 25. Blue M&Ms are Calder and Petra's symbol of secrecy, a sign of their determination to solve the mystery, and represent Fort, Vermeer, and them (p. 89). 26. *Lo!* provides a tie in with frogs, gives Calder and Petra new ways of looking at things, and allows the Lady to communicate with and give clues to Petra (pp. 42, 45, 47–49, 73, 246–247). 27. The puzzle hinges on "twelves." Painting is found under the twelfth stair. There are 12 pentominoes. Calder makes a list of 12 names with 12 letters. Leland Sharpe's message: 1212 (pp. 215, 219, 245, 248–250) 28. Fort's writings cause Calder and Petra to look at things differently, to determine if events are coincidences or related, and help them make connections (pp. 45, 73, 88, 98, 103, 187,

244, 249, 254). 29. The thief demands that the record be corrected, that only 26 of the 35 paintings should be attributed to Vermeer. Ms. Hussey's class and the public study Vermeer and form opinions on the artist's work; pressure is put on museum curators to change wall labels. The Lady speaks to Mrs. Sharpe and Petra because she wants the record corrected. The thief plans the theft based on Ms. Hussey's attribution ideas. Gallery wall labels are changed (pp. 108, 112, 130–131, 238, 254). 30. School assignments lead to studying art. Calder and Petra discover Vermeer, which helps them solve the mystery. The thief and his demands lead to people learning more about art (pp. 27–36, 67, 80, 101, 108–111). **D.** Answers will vary. Refer to the scoring rubric on page 34 of this guide.

Alternative Essay Assessment: Answers will vary. Refer to the scoring rubric on page 34 of this guide.

1. c
   i
   o
   h
   f
   d
   e
   l
   j
   n
   b
   a
   g
   k
   m

2. 5
   3
   10
   6
   1
   4
   9
   8
   7
   2

Linking Novel Units® Student Packets to National and State Reading Assessments

During the past several years, an increasing number of students have faced some form of state-mandated competency testing in reading. Many states now administer state-developed assessments to measure the skills and knowledge emphasized in their particular reading curriculum. This Novel Units® guide includes open-ended comprehension questions that correlate with state-mandated reading assessments. The rubric below provides important information for evaluating responses to open-ended comprehension questions. Teachers may also use scoring rubrics provided for their own state's competency test.

Scoring Rubric for Open-Ended Items

3-Exemplary	Thorough, complete ideas/information Clear organization throughout Logical reasoning/conclusions Thorough understanding of reading task Accurate, complete response
2-Sufficient	Many relevant ideas/pieces of information Clear organization throughout most of response Minor problems in logical reasoning/conclusions General understanding of reading task Generally accurate and complete response
1-Partially Sufficient	Minimally relevant ideas/information Obvious gaps in organization Obvious problems in logical reasoning/conclusions Minimal understanding of reading task Inaccuracies/incomplete response
0-Insufficient	Irrelevant ideas/information No coherent organization Major problems in logical reasoning/conclusions Little or no understanding of reading task Generally inaccurate/incomplete response

Notes

Notes